Build Your Own
Bugs

By Dennis Schatz
Illustrations by Bob Greisen

Andrews and McMeel
A Universal Press Syndicate Company
Kansas City

*To George, who provided my first opportunity to write books
that encourage children to develop higher levels of reasoning*

**Other children's kits
from Andrews and McMeel
by becker&mayer!**
*The Amazing Airplanes Book & Kit
The Amazing Sandcastle Builder's Kit
The American Appaloosa
The Ant Book & See-Through Model
Build Your Own Dinosaurs
The English Thoroughbred
Fun with Ballet
Fun With Electronics
Sleeping Beauty*

With these stamps you can make eight different bugs. To stamp out a bug, follow the "Bug Blueprints" that appear in this book.

It is not necessary that your bugs look exactly like the bugs in this book. Bugs, like humans, look slightly different from one another.

Before using your stamps for the first time, attach the correct sticker to the back of each stamp to properly identify and orient the stamp. In the stamp box, you will find a preprinted sheet of 29 stickers for all of the stamps in this kit.

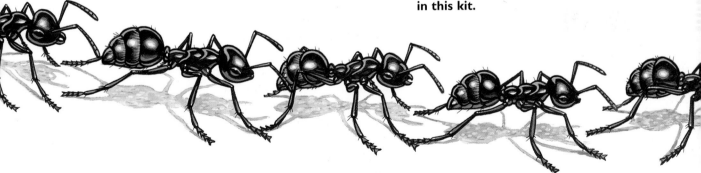

Bugs Dominate the World

People usually hate the creeping, crawling, and buzzing creatures we call bugs. People spray, swat, and stomp on them, wishing they would go away.

But these creatures are essential to life on earth. They eat decaying matter and recycle it for growing plants to use. The animals that people raise to eat produce 12 billion tons of waste each year. This is enough to fill 600 million semitrailer trucks, which, if lined up end to end, would stretch to the moon and back 14 times. Bugs eat almost all of this waste.

Bugs also pollinate crops and other plants, spread seeds that make new plants, and eat many harmful organisms. If humans were to completely die away, the earth would function quite well. But kill all the bugs, and the world environment would collapse in a few months. Ultimately, it would only be inhabited by simple plant life.

Insects, spiders, and the other creepy-crawlies we call bugs are all invertebrates. Invertebrates are animals without backbones. They have a hard skeleton on the outside that protects their soft insides, just as the bones in a human rib cage protect the soft organs inside the body. Invertebrates make up more than 90 percent of the earth's total animal weight.

5

What Is an Insect?

Most people use the word "bug" to mean any type of creepy, crawly creature. Most of these creatures are insects. All insects have six legs, and most have wings. Insects have three main body segments: head, thorax, and abdomen.

The head usually has two types of eyes, two sets of jaws, and a pair of antennae. The compound eyes are made up of hundreds of simple eyes that allow the insect to detect movement in almost every direction at once. The simple eyes measure the brightness of the surrounding light.

One pair of jaws is usually designed for chewing, while the other jaws push or suck food into the mouth. In some insects the jaws are modified to absorb like a sponge, or to pierce like a needle.

The antennae act as the insect's nose, sensing air movement, vibrations, and smells.

The thorax has three segments with a pair of legs connected to each segment. At some time during their lives, most insects have two pairs of wings attached to the thorax, although some have only one pair, and a few have no wings at all.

The abdomen contains the main organs of the insect, including the heart, the digestive, and reproductive systems.

There are more than one million different kinds of insects, many more than the 4,000 different mammals. Almost 200,000 kinds of butterflies and moths exist, as well as almost 300,000 beetles. The term "bug" really refers to just one type of insect, which has wings that are hard at the base and soft at the tips. True bugs also have a feeding tube especially designed for piercing and sucking.

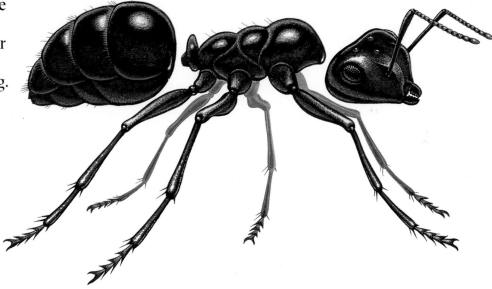

Relatives of Insects

Many insectlike invertebrates, such as spiders, are often mistaken for insects. Spiders have hard outer shells like insects, but the head and thorax are fused into one unit. Spiders have eight legs and no wings or antennae. What they do have in common with insects is that they have legs with joints. This means insects and spiders both belong to a large group of animals called arthropods (ARE-thra-pods), which means "jointed leg."

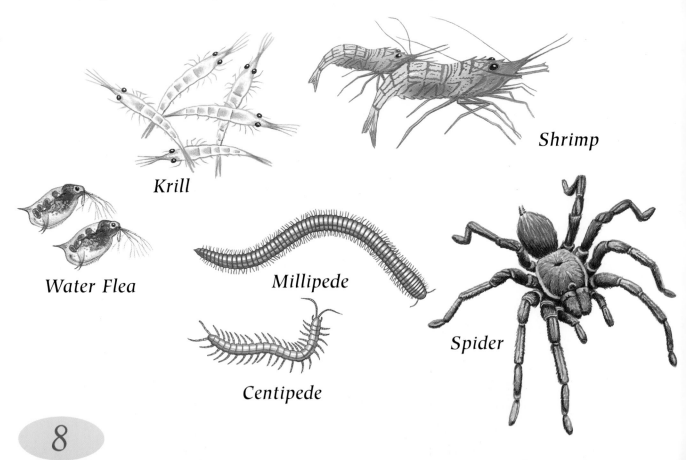

Krill

Shrimp

Water Flea

Millipede

Centipede

Spider

Other members of the arthropod group that are often confused with insects are the centipedes and millipedes. They both have heads with antennae, like the insects, but their bodies are made of many segments. The centipedes have one pair of legs on each segment, while the millipedes have two pairs on each segment.

Many arthropods, including the crab, lobster, and shrimp, live in the ocean. They have at least five pairs of legs and two pairs of antennae. They vary in size from the Japanese giant crab, which is ten feet across, to the water flea, which is the size of the period at the end of this sentence.

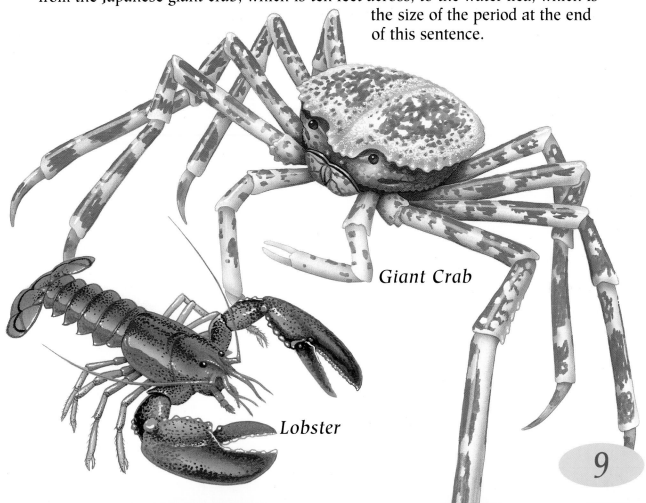

Giant Crab

Lobster

Monarch Butterfly

Butterflies and moths form a single group of insects that consists of almost 200,000 different types. Butterflies fly during the day, and most moths fly at night. When a butterfly lands, it folds its wings together above its body. Moths lay their wings flat out to the sides. Butterfly antennae are always long and thin, ending with a knob. Moth antennae are often feathery looking.

Butterflies are usually very colorful, while moths have subdued coloring. The coloring helps scare predators away or hides them from predators. The monarch butterfly's bright color tells other animals that it might contain poison. The color and pattern on the wings of the Pine Hawk moth make it hard to see on the bark of the pine trees where it often rests. The color on the wings of both insects is made by thousands of scales lined up like shingles on a roof.

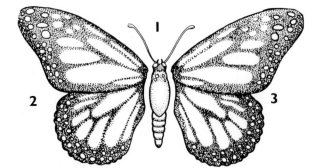

Butterflies and moths begin their lives looking very different than they do as adults. Eggs from the adult insect hatch into caterpillars that do little but eat. When the caterpillar is finished growing, it forms a protective covering. Inside the protective covering, the caterpillar completely changes its shape. It forms wings, and its mouth, which was designed for chewing leaves, often becomes a long tube designed to suck fluids from flowers.

Most butterflies and moths only live for a short time, although the monarch butterfly lives longer and is known for its long-distance migration of over 1,000 miles from the northern United States to Mexico.

Carpenter Ant

Ants live in large colonies that contain as many as 100,000 members. They have strong jaws that can give a nasty bite. Some ants even inject acid into the bite; that makes it hurt more.

Streams of ants are often seen searching for food as far away as 300 feet from their nest, and may be carrying large objects up to 50 times their weight. If humans could perform similar feats, a six-foot, 200-pound human would walk more than eight miles each day to find food and be able to lift a 10,000-pound truck.

Each ant nest is started by a single, winged queen ant that leaves the old nest shortly after it is born, accompanied by several winged males. The queen mates with one of the males once and stores enough sperm to last the rest of her life. The queen may live for 15 years, but the male dies soon after mating. The queen breaks off her wings and begins a new nest that is built and maintained by wingless female ants that cannot lay eggs. These worker females also gather food and take care of the unhatched ants.

Ladybird Beetle

Ladybird beetles are better known as ladybugs. The name ladybug is misleading because ladybugs are not true bugs. They are a type of beetle. Like all other beetles, the ladybird beetle wears a heavy coat of armor. One set of its two pairs of wings is not used to fly, but is a hard wing case that covers the soft second pair of wings hidden below. When the ladybird wants to fly, it opens its wing case and then extends its soft wings to fly. Thus, it takes the ladybird beetle a long time to fly away, making flight more a means to change location rather than to escape from predators.

Most people think of a ladybird beetle as being red with many black spots. However, there are more than 350 different types that vary from red to orange to yellow, containing between two and fifteen spots. Ladybird beetles often live two or three years and assemble by the thousands to hibernate through the winter under rocks or fallen logs.

Ladybird beetles are some of the most useful insects to humans because many types feed exclusively on aphids, which are small sucking insects that destroy crops. Farmers will often spread millions of ladybird beetles throughout a crop to eat aphids. Three thousand ladybird beetles can protect 100 orange trees, which produce 70,000 oranges each year.

Stag Beetle

Beetles are the most common type of insect with over 300,000 different types. The stag beetle is another member of the heavily armored beetle family. It is one of the larger examples, with the male being more than 1½ inches long. The name comes from the large horns that are used like the antlers of a stag deer to defend its mate and territory from other male stag beetles. The horns are actually enlarged jaws that are used to grasp the opponent around the middle so it can be thrown off the piece of rotting wood that is the winner's prize.

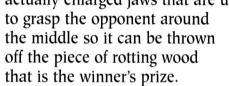

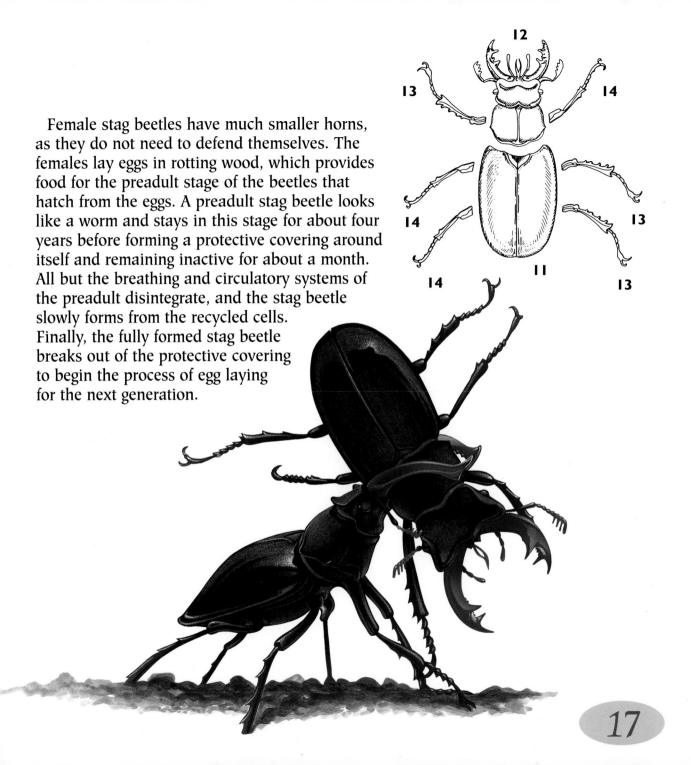

Female stag beetles have much smaller horns, as they do not need to defend themselves. The females lay eggs in rotting wood, which provides food for the preadult stage of the beetles that hatch from the eggs. A preadult stag beetle looks like a worm and stays in this stage for about four years before forming a protective covering around itself and remaining inactive for about a month. All but the breathing and circulatory systems of the preadult disintegrate, and the stag beetle slowly forms from the recycled cells. Finally, the fully formed stag beetle breaks out of the protective covering to begin the process of egg laying for the next generation.

17

Green Darner Dragonfly

Dragonflies are the insect most closely related to the first flying insects that appeared on the earth some 600 million years ago, well before any of the big land animals such as dinosaurs, reptiles, or mammals. Today, the largest dragonflies have wingspans a little over eight inches long, but fossils of dragonfly-like insects show wingspans of over two feet.

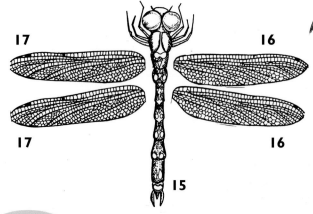

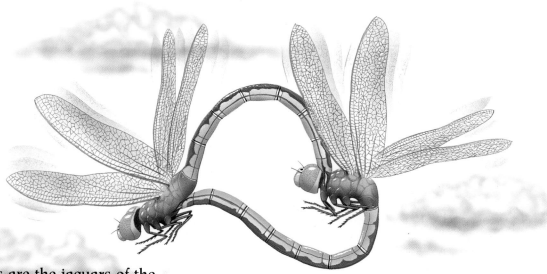

Dragonflies are the jaguars of the insect world. They can fly at an amazing 25 miles per hour and can change direction quickly. Their six legs work together to form a basket to capture other insects in midflight. Dragonflies can capture small flies just before dark when no humans can see the flies. It is not clear whether the dragonfly sees the fly or detects the air motion caused by the fly's movement.

Most dragonflies live as an adult for only a few weeks. During the preadult stage, the dragonfly may spend as many as three years living underwater. It has no wings, breathes through gills like a fish, and feeds on small fish or insects. When fully grown, the dragonfly crawls up the stem of a water plant and breaks out of its old skin, transformed into the new shape of the adult dragonfly.

After several days, the adult dragonfly chooses a mate, and they fly together with the ends of their abdomens joined together. Sperm from the male transfers to the female. The female then lays her eggs in the water, one at a time.

Greenbottle Fly

Flies are the acrobats of the insect world. They can fly backward or hover over a single spot. Suckerlike pads between the claws of each foot even allow them to walk upside down on the ceiling. Unlike most other insects with wings, the fly has only two wings rather than four. Instead of two hind wings, it has small drumstick structures called halteres, which are used for flight control like the spinning gyroscope in an airplane.

The compound eyes of a fly contain hundreds of simple eyes. This provides many overlapping images of the fly's surroundings, allowing it to detect even the slightest movement. Its excellent vision plus its ability to move quickly make the fly very hard to catch.

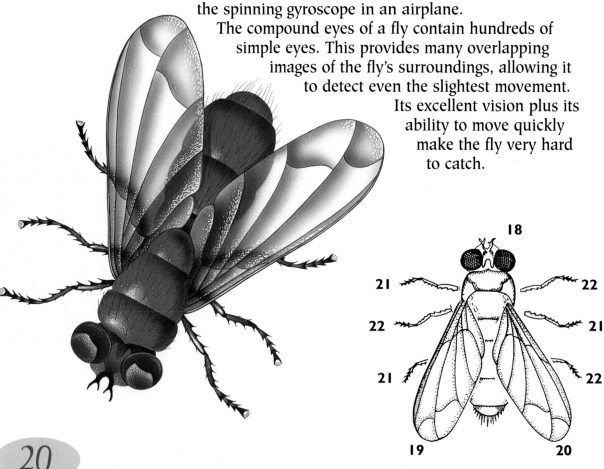

18
21
22
22
21
21
22
19
20

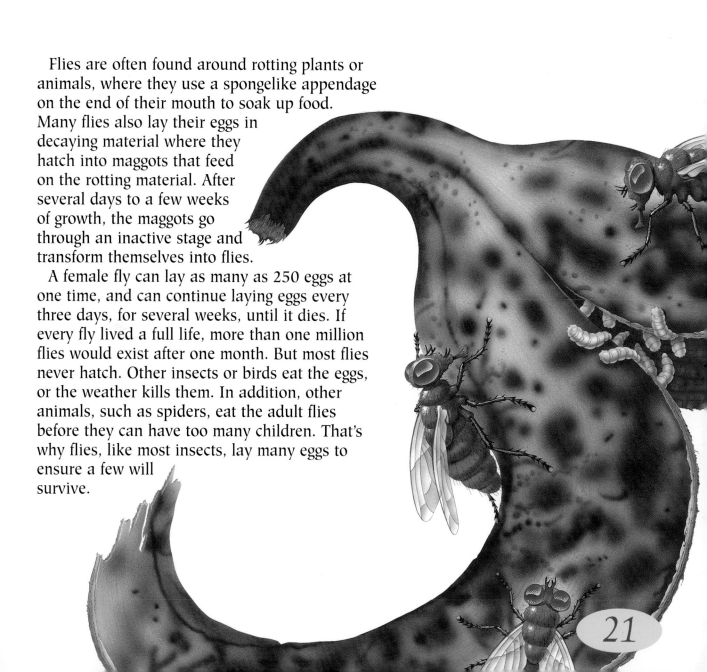

Flies are often found around rotting plants or animals, where they use a spongelike appendage on the end of their mouth to soak up food. Many flies also lay their eggs in decaying material where they hatch into maggots that feed on the rotting material. After several days to a few weeks of growth, the maggots go through an inactive stage and transform themselves into flies.

A female fly can lay as many as 250 eggs at one time, and can continue laying eggs every three days, for several weeks, until it dies. If every fly lived a full life, more than one million flies would exist after one month. But most flies never hatch. Other insects or birds eat the eggs, or the weather kills them. In addition, other animals, such as spiders, eat the adult flies before they can have too many children. That's why flies, like most insects, lay many eggs to ensure a few will survive.

Anopheles Mosquito

The mosquito is a blood-sucking fly. Its mouth combines a piercing needle and a sucking straw. The mosquito does not need blood to survive. It lives its life of several weeks sampling the juices of plants. But after the female mosquito mates, it must have a drop of blood to mix with the eggs to give them the nourishment required to hatch.

After finding a source of blood—often a human—the mosquito uses its sharp needlelike mouth to pierce the skin. It injects a substance that allows the blood to flow freely and sucks in a drop of blood to mix with its eggs. The substance that the mosquito injects into the wound causes a bump that often itches.

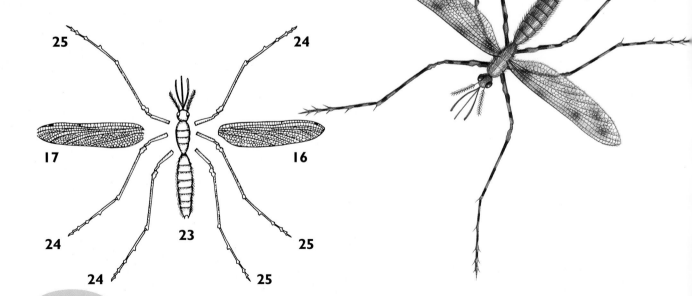

25 24

17 16

24 23 25

24 25

The female then lays her eggs in a quiet pool of water. After several days the mosquitoes hatch. The preadults look nothing like adult mosquitoes. They are tube-shaped and live completely in the water where they swim by wiggling. Periodically, they come to the surface to breathe air through snorkels in the tail end of their abdomens. After several weeks of growing larger in the water, the preadults build cases around themselves and transform themselves into adult mosquitoes.

The adult mosquito has fine hairs on much of its body. These hairs are used to detect air movement. The mosquito senses the movement caused by the motion of your hand and flies away before you get near it. These hairs also detect the buzzing of other mosquitoes. This helps mates find each other, since every different kind of mosquito has a unique buzz.

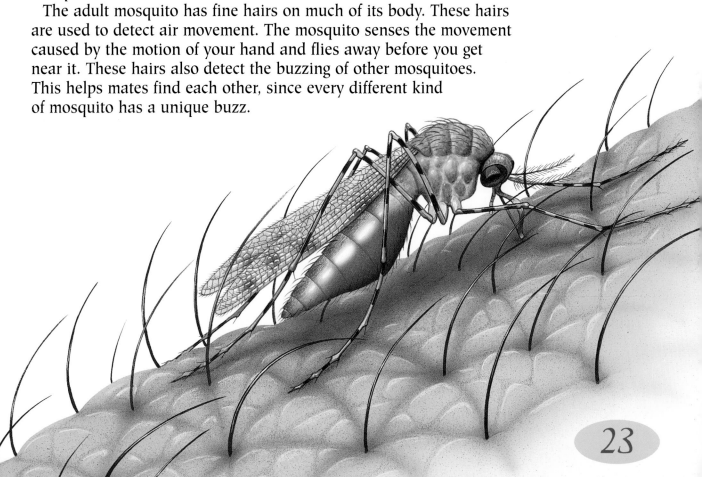

Orb Weaver Spider

Spiders can be divided into two different types, either hunters or waiters. The hunters have keen eyesight and stalk their prey the way a lion does. Scorpions and tarantulas are good examples of hunter spiders. Waiter spiders build webs and wait for their prey to fly or walk into them. Waiters usually have poor eyesight but a very sensitive sense of touch that detects when the smallest of insects is caught in the web.

The most common kind of spider is the orb weaver, which constructs a large circular web between the branches of a tree or in the corner of a building. The silk for the web is produced by six small openings at the end of the abdomen. The silk is a liquid until exposed to air, where it hardens into a tough thread. This silk is similar to the silk used in clothes, and is so strong that some people use it to weave into ropes for fishing nets.

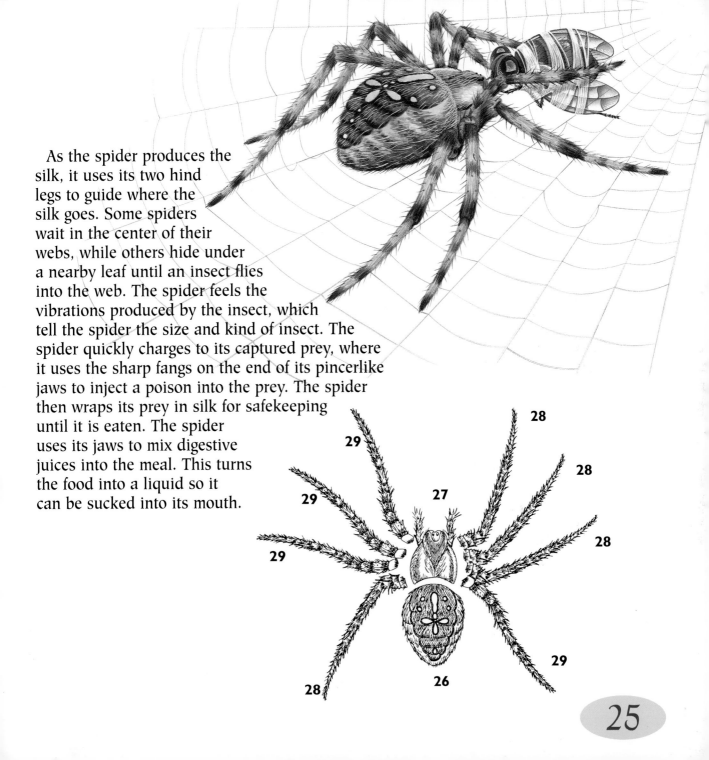

As the spider produces the silk, it uses its two hind legs to guide where the silk goes. Some spiders wait in the center of their webs, while others hide under a nearby leaf until an insect flies into the web. The spider feels the vibrations produced by the insect, which tell the spider the size and kind of insect. The spider quickly charges to its captured prey, where it uses the sharp fangs on the end of its pincerlike jaws to inject a poison into the prey. The spider then wraps its prey in silk for safekeeping until it is eaten. The spider uses its jaws to mix digestive juices into the meal. This turns the food into a liquid so it can be sucked into its mouth.

28

29

27

29

28

29

28

28

29

26

25

Insect Lifestyles

W hat each insect or spider calls home varies greatly and tells us much about how each creature lives its life. Ants live in large colonies and make their homes in many different places. Carpenter ants chew holes in wood to make chambers for living.

A tour of an ant nest reveals many interconnected chambers. In the deepest recesses of the nest, worker ants groom and feed the queen, while other workers tend to her newly laid eggs. In other chambers, ants ready to hatch send a chemical signal so that workers will tear into the cocoons to help the new ants out. Other ants may be building new chambers for the growing colony. Food-gathering workers return from the surrounding area with meals for everyone.

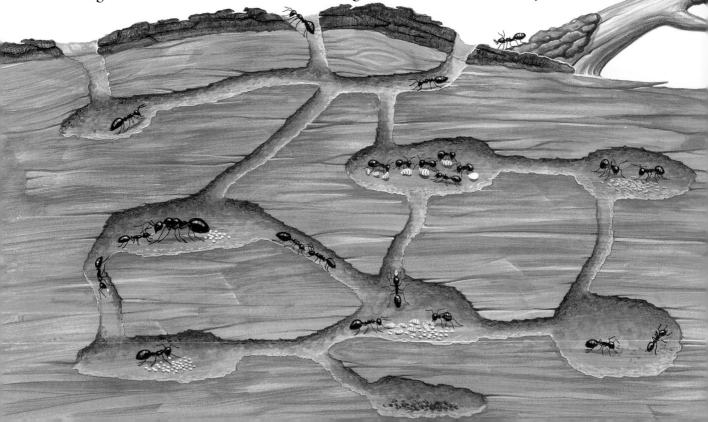

In contrast to the ant, a spider's life is very solitary. Each spider builds its own web, often remaking it each night. From its position on one branch of a tree, the spider lets out a thread of silk, hoping the wind will carry the end to another branch. When the silk finally attaches to another object, the spider reinforces it with several more threads. The spider then moves to the center of this bridge and drops straight down until it can attach a thread of silk to something. This thread is used to pull down one of the threads from the main bridge to form a Y shape. The center point of the Y forms a hub for spokes of silk that hold the circular spiral that makes the main part of the web. Finally, the spider retires to the center of the web, or to a nearby leaf, to wait for its meal to get caught in the web.

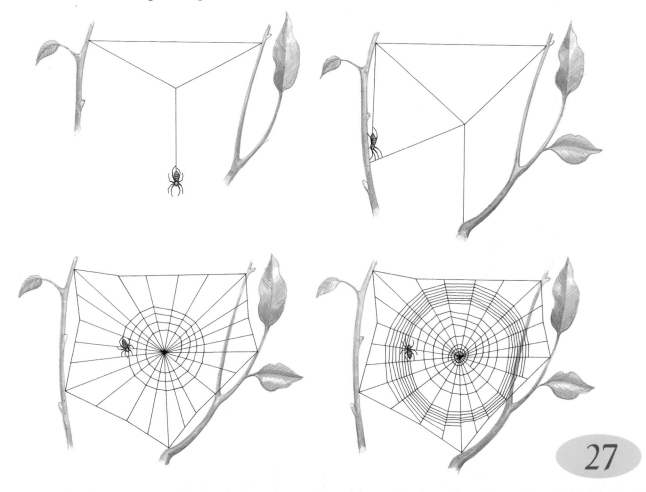

Insect Life Cycles
The Dragonfly

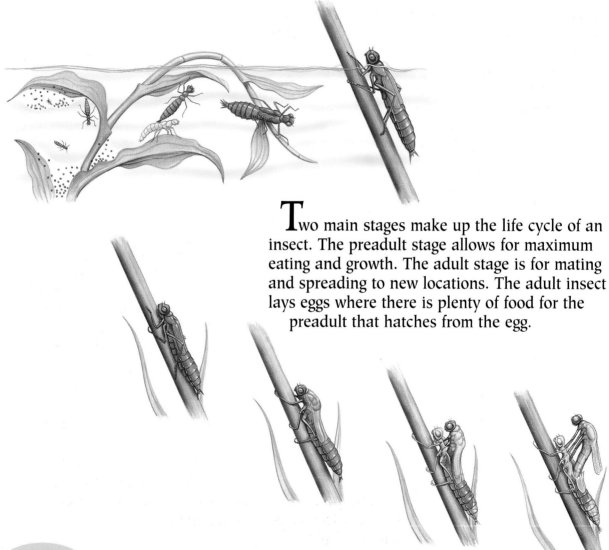

Two main stages make up the life cycle of an insect. The preadult stage allows for maximum eating and growth. The adult stage is for mating and spreading to new locations. The adult insect lays eggs where there is plenty of food for the preadult that hatches from the egg.

The hard external skeleton of an insect does not grow along with its body, so an insect must periodically shed its skin. When an insect outgrows its skeleton, the inner layers dissolve and the insect swallows air or water until the skeleton cracks open. The insect then wiggles out of its old skeleton, and secretes a substance to harden the new, soft skeleton.

Some insects go through a gradual change in which their bodies slowly change each time the preadult sheds its skin. The dragonfly deposits eggs in pools of water. The preadult dragonfly, called a nymph, feeds on small fish and insects in the water. The nymph begins to show bumps, which are miniature wings, on the back of its body after it has shed its skin about four times.

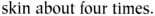

When the nymph is fully grown, it climbs out of the water onto a plant. Under the cover of night, its head and front legs emerge from the old skin, and then come its wings, which are crumpled, soft, and damp. The dragonfly uses its new front legs to pull the rest of its body free. It begins pumping fluid into its wings and body, which expand to almost twice as long as they were just before shedding its skin. After a few hours, the wings harden and are ready for flight.

29

Insect Life Cycles
The Butterfly

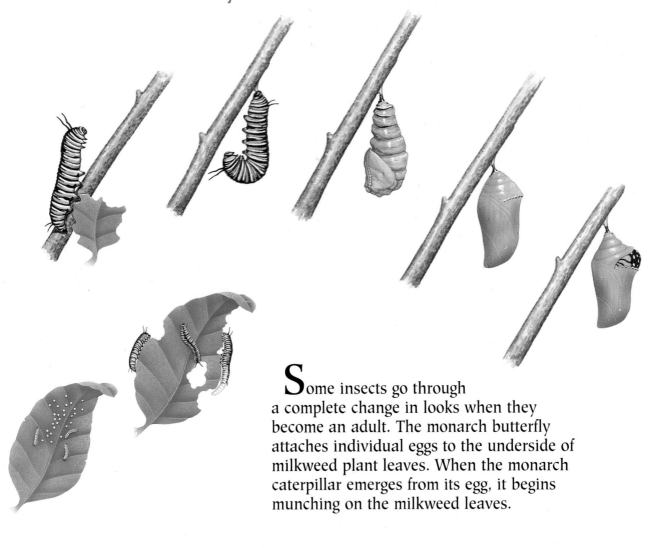

Some insects go through a complete change in looks when they become an adult. The monarch butterfly attaches individual eggs to the underside of milkweed plant leaves. When the monarch caterpillar emerges from its egg, it begins munching on the milkweed leaves.

After a few weeks of eating milkweed leaves and shedding its skin, the caterpillar finds a protected spot under a milkweed leaf to attach a small patch of silk. Hanging by its tail from the silk, the caterpillar bends its body into the shape of the letter J. Its outer skin slowly splits open and falls off to reveal a green, hard covering. Only the digestive and circulatory systems remain inside the covering. The rest of the caterpillar dissolves and transforms itself into a butterfly.

After a number of days, the covering begins to clear, and the pattern on the monarch butterfly wings can be seen. A damp, crumpled butterfly finally breaks out of the covering. The butterfly is ready to fly after pumping fluid into its wings to expand them and secreting a chemical to harden them. With its new ability to fly, the butterfly easily finds a mate and spreads its eggs to new milkweed plants far from where it was born as a caterpillar.

Create Your Own Insect

Although more than a million different types of insects are known to exist, scientists think that there are yet many millions more to be discovered, especially in tropical rain forests. Enjoy using the stamps in this kit to create new insects that have yet to be discovered.